NATURAL LIVING

NEAL'S YARD
COVENT GARDEN
REMEDIES

BEAUTIFY

Penguin
Random
House

Editors Martha Burley, Libby Brown
Designers Alison Gardner, Tessa Bindloss,
Laura Buscemi
Jacket Designer Vanessa Hamilton
Producer, Pre-Production Rebecca Fallowfield
Production Controller Isobel Reid
Special Sales Creative Project Manager
Alison Donovan

Content previously published in *Neal's Yard Beauty Book*
(2015) by Dorling Kindersley Limited
80 Strand, London, WC2R 0RL

2 4 6 8 10 9 7 5 3 1
001 – 309663 – Dec/2017

Copyright © 2015, 2017
Dorling Kindersley Limited
A Penguin Random House Company

All rights reserved. No part of this publication may be
reproduced, stored in, or introduced into a retrieval
system, or transmitted in any form, or by any means
(electronic, mechanical, photocopying, recording or
otherwise), without the prior written permission of
the copyright owner.

A CIP catalogue record for this book is available
from the British Library.

ISBN 978-0-2413-3409-6

Printed and bound in China

A WORLD OF IDEAS
SEE ALL THERE IS TO KNOW
www.dk.com

DISCLAIMER: See page 48

CONTENTS

WHAT IS BEAUTY?

Ask the question "what is beauty?", and you'll get a multitude of different answers. Everybody has a theory. In fact, mankind has been searching for the answer for a long time. The truth is, throughout your life, your own concept of beauty will change. What was appropriate for you at one age or stage of life may not be appropriate at another.

CHANGING PERCEPTIONS

Less than a century ago, the dictionary defined beauty as "properties pleasing the eye, the ear, the intellect, the aesthetic faculty, or the moral sense". Today, the default definition of beauty is narrow, focusing only on what is pleasing to the eye. This change has gained momentum because, for a long time, beauty, even natural beauty, has been defined by the media, Hollywood, and the globalized beauty industry. And yet, when we think of beauty as outwardly focused – a mask that we put on, or what we project in order to please others – we make a game for ourselves that is impossible to win.

Research shows that for most females, the inner beauty critic arrives at age 14 and continues to erode her self-esteem as she ages. This erosion has a profound effect on health and well-being. Research also shows that people who accept their looks are happier and healthier – the stress of fighting who you are can affect your health, which in turn affects physical beauty.

WORKING WITH NATURE

A revolution seeks to redefine beauty as natural and holistic, and more reflective of our needs, emotions, and perceptions. This leaves behind a static, one-size-fits-all philosophy and embraces a broader appreciation of diverse human beings

PRO-AGEING

The notion that youth equates to beauty is not sustainable in a world where the population is ageing. Research shows that interest in youth potions and invasive surgeries falls off after the age of 45. Older women, it seems, are more interested in looking good for their age than looking eternally young. They are also more likely to try therapeutic beauty treatments, such as massage or facials. These therapies don't just improve the appearance, they also embrace the inner self and promote a sense of well-being.

of all ages and cultures. It has also triggered a movement away from synthetic and mass-produced beauty products made from polluting and increasingly scarce petrochemical ingredients, to those made from safe and sustainable natural substances.

As many of us become environmentally aware, we know that there is no real beauty if the means to achieve it are ugly. Animal testing, toxic industrial chemicals, avoidable waste, science experiments such as GMO or nanotechnology that turn customers into lab rats, and lies on the labels are all ugly.

Our increasing interest in natural beauty, which mirrors an increased awareness of being environmentally friendly, is a positive and inspiring cultural shift, and a valuable alternative to plastic beauty.

Concern for what we put in our bodies, and a recent trend for natural and wholesome foods, extends into concern for what we are applying to our bodies. It is hard to feel healthy when one subsists on a diet of refined and highly processed junk food. It is just as hard to feel beautiful when one uses "junk" beauty products, made with petrochemicals or synthetic fragrances that some studies say disrupt the body's hormonal or nervous systems, cause cancer, provoke allergies, or cause harm to your unborn baby.

FROM THE INSIDE OUT

Wanting to be sure of what is actually in the products we use has started another revolution in beauty – an interest in making our own products from known and trusted ingredients. Nature provides much of what we need to stay beautiful in the form of healthy unadulterated foods but also in the form of ingredients such as luxurious oils and plant essences – and you may be surprised to find that some of the best beauty ingredients are already in your kitchen cupboards.

The recipes and tips in his book show how effective natural products are and how you can use them in your day-to-day life. Combining these in creative ways gives you total control over exactly what you are putting on your skin and hair, and is an art and a science that is within your grasp.

First and foremost, beauty should be something we do for ourselves, to feel better, to look better, to express what's inside us, to occasionally treat and indulge. Real beauty should promote a happier, healthier, more relaxed, more confident and comfortable "you". Studies show that our concepts of what is beautiful and what we think others find beautiful are often miles apart. Reclaiming the notion of natural beauty, then, could be seen as a process of narrowing that gap between who you are on the inside and what others see.

JASMINE
Antioxidant-rich jasmine can help to condition, heal, and soothe your skin.

ROSE ABSOLUTE EXTRACT
With a delicate fragrance, rose absolute can combat the signs of ageing.

ECO CONCERNS

Many chemicals in conventional products, such as hormone-disrupting parabens, also harm the planet – either through unsustainable sourcing, during their manufacture, or when they are washed into drains and into our water supplies. As we become more aware of the damage that humankind has done to the planet, it is clear that trashing the planet in the name of vanity simply isn't beautiful.

THE SECRET LIFE OF YOUR SKIN

Your skin is alive and dynamic. It breathes, grows, and changes. It protects the body from bacteria, viruses, and pollutants, takes in nutrients and, through sweat, helps remove toxins. It regulates body temperature, manufactures vitamin D from sunlight, and provides information through touch and pain. Every day the skin reflects and reacts to what you eat and drink, your exposure to the elements, how you sleep, the stress you are under, and your general health.

UNDER YOUR SKIN

The skin consists of three layers: the epidermis, the dermis, and the subcutis. Each layer has particular functions that help skin to renew, react, and protect your body.

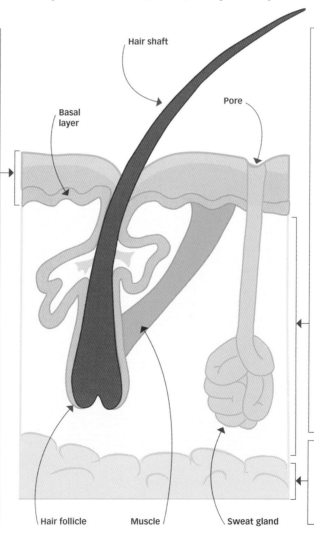

EPIDERMIS

An elastic layer on the outside, the epidermis is continually regenerating. It is made up of a number of different kinds of cells.

KERATINOCYTES

The main cells of the epidermis, keratinocytes are formed by cell division at its base. New cells continually move towards the surface. Gradually, as they move they die, are flattened, and are sloughed off. This process takes around 14 days (longer as we age).

CORNEOCYTES

Flattened dead keratinocytes, corneocytes make up a tough, protective, and virtually waterproof layer called the *stratum corneum* or horny layer. This layer continually renews and is sloughed off. In fact, each of us sloughs off millions of dead skin cells every day.

MELANOCYTES

These produce the pigment melanin that protects against UV radiation and gives skin its colour. Exposure to the sun stimulates increased melanin production, and this results in the skin becoming darker – or tanned. When melanin is unable to absorb all the ultra-violet rays, because of prolonged and unaccustomed exposure, the skin is damaged and it will burn.

DERMIS

The inner layer of the skin is composed of connective tissue, containing both elastin (the fibres that give the qualities of stretch and suppleness to the skin) and collagen (the fibres that provide strength). The dermis also contains numerous blood vessels, follicles, and glands.

HAIR FOLLICLES

These are pits where hair grows. Protective hair plays a role in temperature regulation.

SEBACEOUS GLANDS

These produce sebum (a natural oil) to keep hairs free from dust and bacteria. Sebum and sweat make up the surface "film" of the skin.

SWEAT GLANDS

Sweat is produced in the glands and travels via sweat ducts to openings in the epidermis called pores. They play a role in temperature regulation. Specific types of sweat glands called apocrine glands occur in hair parts of the body and only become active during puberty.

SUBCUTIS

Under the dermis lies the subcutis or subcutaneous layer, which is made up of connective tissue and fat. It is a good insulator.

Hair shaft

Basal layer

Pore

Hair follicle

Muscle

Sweat gland

WORK WITH YOUR SKIN

You should not see normal skin changes as problems that need to be fixed. Try to stop obsessing over minute and transient shifts in skin tone and colour, and adopt a sensible approach to skin care. Some things are beyond our control – how skin ages, for instance, is a complicated process involving a number of internal and external factors, some of which are within our control, many of which are not.

Ageing causes a decrease in collagen and elastin, the "scaffolding" of the skin, causing the skin to wrinkle and sag. Gravity can also make loose skin around eyes and jowls fall even more. Aged skin also appears more translucent because of the decrease in the number of pigment-containing cells (melanocytes). It is also thinner and more fragile, and at increased risk of injury and less able to repair itself.

Accepting the complex secret life of your skin and responding to it with a "from the inside out" approach is not only sensible and healthy, but can also make the difference between being at war or at peace with your skin.

MAKE PEACE WITH YOUR SKIN

If you want beautiful skin – whether it is youthful or mature – then you need to identify and work with the skin's natural rhythms (see pp8-9) and support them with healthy lifestyle choices.

Have a lot of good-quality sleep, which is vital for skin health. Don't only focus on the number of hours, but think about the quality of sleep. A chronic lack of good-quality sleep can age skin by as much as 10 years.

Relieve stress and see a miraculous effect on skin. Help your health and appearance by addressing stress and anxiety, perhaps by engaging in a hobby that absorbs you.

Drink at least 2 litres (3½ pints) of water a day to make a big difference to the radiance and moisture of your skin.

Avoid cigarettes and alcohol, which are highly damaging. Both can dehydrate the skin and interfere with its ability to utilize nutrients – just take a look at your skin after a heavy night out.

Use good-quality skin products that make use of gentle natural cleansing agents and natural oils and plant extracts instead of industrial petrochemical derivatives.

Eat healthily because your diet is influential on the health of your skin in both the short and the long term. For instance, studies show that diets that are high in sugar can make the skin look older. In contrast, diets rich in healthy omega-3 fats can protect against sun damage and even acne.

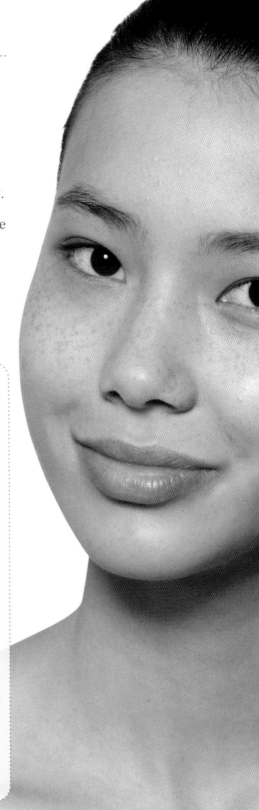

THE RHYTHMS OF YOUR SKIN

As the largest organ in the body, your skin has its own rhythms. It is tempting to try to tame and bully your skin into submission, but getting in touch with its natural rhythms is the most straightforward path to a healthier complexion.

THE DAILY CYCLE

Healthy, normal skin can change on almost an hourly basis. The clocks below show just how regularly your skin changes in the cycle of a day.

AM

You're much more likely to have an allergic skin reaction in the morning than in the afternoon.

AT 8am
Your skin is less likely to absorb products at 8am than in the afternoon, so it is not a good time to apply rich nourishing masks and serums.

PM

Skin is calmer in the late afternoon and evening. However, water loss is high at night, so apply moisturising creams and serums before you go to sleep.

9pm–MIDNIGHT
Skin is more sensitive to histamine late in the evening, which means itchy skin conditions such as dermatitis may be worse. If you need a skin-allergy test, schedule it for as late in the day as possible. Your skin is more acidic, and as a result oilier, when you sleep. Don't make the problem worse by using harsh acidic peels and scrubs before bedtime.

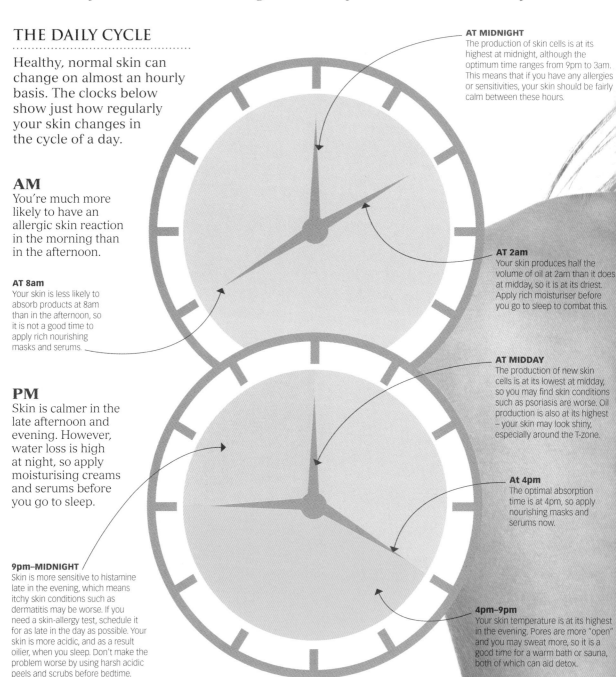

AT MIDNIGHT
The production of skin cells is at its highest at midnight, although the optimum time ranges from 9pm to 3am. This means that if you have any allergies or sensitivities, your skin should be fairly calm between these hours.

AT 2am
Your skin produces half the volume of oil at 2am than it does at midday, so it is at its driest. Apply rich moisturiser before you go to sleep to combat this.

AT MIDDAY
The production of new skin cells is at its lowest at midday, so you may find skin conditions such as psoriasis are worse. Oil production is also at its highest – your skin may look shiny, especially around the T-zone.

At 4pm
The optimal absorption time is at 4pm, so apply nourishing masks and serums now.

4pm–9pm
Your skin temperature is at its highest in the evening. Pores are more "open" and you may sweat more, so it is a good time for a warm bath or sauna, both of which can aid detox.

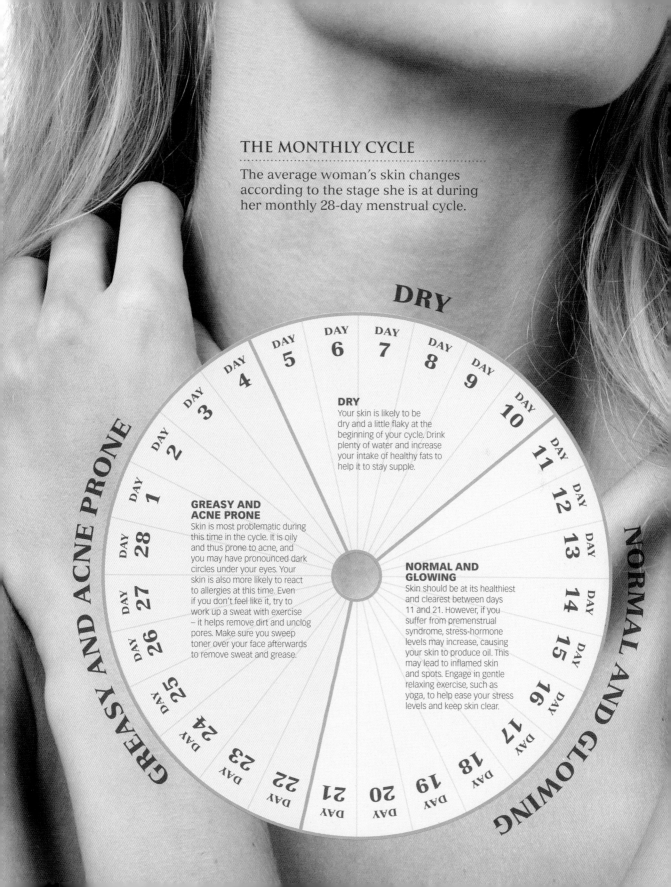

THE MONTHLY CYCLE

The average woman's skin changes according to the stage she is at during her monthly 28-day menstrual cycle.

DRY

GREASY AND ACNE PRONE

NORMAL AND GLOWING

DAY 4
DAY 5
DAY 6
DAY 7
DAY 8
DAY 9
DAY 10
DAY 3
DAY 2
DAY 1
DAY 28
DAY 27
DAY 26
DAY 25
DAY 24
DAY 23
DAY 22
DAY 21
DAY 20
DAY 19
DAY 18
DAY 17
DAY 16
DAY 15
DAY 14
DAY 13
DAY 12
DAY 11

DRY
Your skin is likely to be dry and a little flaky at the beginning of your cycle. Drink plenty of water and increase your intake of healthy fats to help it to stay supple.

GREASY AND ACNE PRONE
Skin is most problematic during this time in the cycle. It is oily and thus prone to acne, and you may have pronounced dark circles under your eyes. Your skin is also more likely to react to allergies at this time. Even if you don't feel like it, try to work up a sweat with exercise – it helps remove dirt and unclog pores. Make sure you sweep toner over your face afterwards to remove sweat and grease.

NORMAL AND GLOWING
Skin should be at its healthiest and clearest between days 11 and 21. However, if you suffer from premenstrual syndrome, stress-hormone levels may increase, causing your skin to produce oil. This may lead to inflamed skin and spots. Engage in gentle relaxing exercise, such as yoga, to help ease your stress levels and keep skin clear.

THE KIT YOU NEED

Discover everything you need to create and apply natural beauty products like a professional. It is so easy to make a vast array of fantastic products with very little specialized equipment. You could also simplify your beauty kit, leaving yourself with basic, versatile tools that help to give perfect results.

MAKE YOUR OWN PRODUCTS

It is hugely satisfying, cheap, and fun to make your own products. You have full control over the ingredients that you use and the source, quality, and quantity. Much of the equipment you need is probably already in your kitchen cupboards. It is fine to use the same tools for food preparation and cosmetics, provided everything is completely clean.

KEEPING PRODUCTS

Use all products within a short period of time as they will perish more quickly than conventional products. Make only enough for personal use or for gifts.

Fresh ingredient-based products should be used on the same day, but you could use them throughout the day and keep them in the fridge between uses.

Oil-based products, such as balms, keep for up to 6 months. Store in an airtight container in a cool, dry, and dark place.

Recipes containing water, such as emulsion-based creams, perish quickly. Store them in airtight containers and keep them in the fridge.

THERMOMETER Use a food-grade cooking thermometer to heat mineral water to 80ºC (175ºF) – the optimum temperature to create water-based emulsions.

HAND-HELD WHISK Use a balloon whisk to mix emulsions to the right consistency.

STICK BLENDER Save time and energy by using a plastic or metal stick blender – these are cheap and easy to clean. They are useful for making emulsions and soaps.

LIDS, DROPPERS, ATOMIZERS, AND PUMPS Finding the right dispenser for your product is key – think about how much of the product you need for application and match that with the appropriate closure.

TEA POT Use a tea pot with a filter inside or use a tea strainer to make healthy herbal infusions to drink or use in products.

MOULDS Try specialized silicone moulds for soaps, bath bombs, or melts. These are very durable. Ice-cube trays or baking trays are also suitable.

STERILIZED JARS, BOTTLES, AND CONTAINERS Use specialized vessels or sterilize whatever you have to hand. All products keep for longer in containers with airtight lids.

BAIN-MARIE Essentially just a glass bowl that sits inside a saucepan, a bain-marie is necessary for most balm, cream, and lotion recipes. Make sure that the bottom of the glass bowl never touches the boiling water.

KILNER JARS These are especially useful for scrubs and powders, as they are airtight and keep contents fresh for longer.

APPLY YOUR BEAUTY PRODUCTS

You can use your fingers or hands to apply many products – this allows you to control the pressure and movement. However, you do need some simple and cheap beauty tools for certain tasks. Use organic and non-animal derived cotton and brushes where possible, and always make sure that wooden tools have been sustainably sourced. You may also need an easy-to-wash hairband to keep products out of your hair.

COTTON WOOL PADS AND BALLS Versatile cotton wool pads and balls are useful for removing make-up and applying cleansing products. Always buy organic.

POWDER PUFF After bathing, smooth body powders over dry skin with a powder puff.

FLANNEL OR MUSLIN CLOTH Use to remove products from the skin. Always wash flannels and muslin cloths thoroughly every time they have been in contact with the skin.

COTTON BUDS The perfect tool to erase mistakes and blend eyeliner and eyeshadow. You can even use cotton buds to apply lip colour.

HAIRBRUSH Use a natural-bristle brush to brush dry or wet hair. Avoid pig bristles where possible.

DRY BODY BRUSH Once a week, invigorate the skin all over the body before you bathe. Use a long-handled brush for difficult-to-reach parts.

FOUNDATION BRUSH This is a multi-purpose brush that you can use to apply make-up and clay-based masks.

BLUSHER BRUSH Use this brush to apply powder and/or mineral blusher to the cheek area.

POWDER BRUSH Use this brush to apply loose, pressed, or mineral powder to the face and décolleté (the neck, shoulders, chest, and upper back).

EYESHADOW BRUSH Apply eyeshadow and contour the eye area using a variety of eyeshadow brushes.

EYESHADOW BLENDING BRUSH Create a refined finish by using this brush to blend your eyeshadow.

SMUDGE BRUSH Soften and blend eyeliner and apply eyeshadow to the lower lash line with this brush.

EYELINER BRUSH Use this brush to apply eyeliner to both the upper and lower lash lines.

ANGLED BRUSH Use a small angled brush to apply brow powder and eyeliner, and a large brush to add contour to the face.

LIP BRUSH Apply lipstick, lip gloss, and lip stains with this brush.

WHAT'S YOUR SKIN TYPE?

Identifying your skin type is a great starting point to use to plan a skin-care regime and make adjustments to your lifestyle and diet. You probably have some idea of your skin type – maybe you've taken a quiz, looked at a comparison chart, or had a beauty consultation. However, it is a good idea to review it regularly, as your type is likely to change over time.

IDENTIFY YOUR TYPE

Your skin type is not set in stone and should be seen as more of a guideline than a rule. However, this simple flowchart helps to determine your basic type.

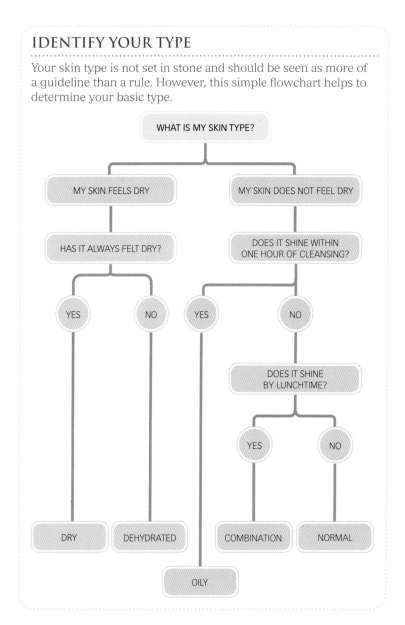

WHAT IS NORMAL?

Many of us try everything we can to change our skin type to "normal". From a beauty perspective, normal skin is shorthand for skin that is blemish-free, glowing, resilient when temporarily exposed to external challenges such as sun and wind, balanced between too oily and too dry, and toned in a way that defies age – at least for a little while.

Everything we do to improve our skin is geared towards getting our skin to that magical "normal" state, but the truth is that knowing your skin type is only a starting point. It's a basic guideline that can help you choose skin-care products as well as help you to make lifestyle decisions, such as how much sun exposure you should have.

Identifying your skin type is a helpful starting point when learning how to care for your skin.

INFLUENCES ON YOUR SKIN

Hereditary factors determine a great deal about our skin type, as well as its colour, tendencies, and susceptibility to certain skin problems. We can often use this knowledge of our family history in preventative care. For example, if you know your mother had fair skin and it was prone to sunburn, and you have a very similar skin type to her, you can take special precautions.

However, inheritance is not the whole story. Diet and skin-care routines are also important factors in the health of the skin. Skin types can change throughout your life too, most dramatically during periods of hormonal upheaval such as puberty, pregnancy, and menopause.

As a living organ, the skin is dynamic and responds to what's going on both inside and outside your body. If you think you have "sensitive skin", you may be reacting to a dietary allergen or, more commonly, an irritant in a cosmetic or toiletry. Remove the allergen and your skin type may become something else entirely.

NORMAL SKIN

Normal skin is soft, smooth, supple, and not prone to eruptions. It should also have a healthy glow. It requires a low-maintenance daily regime of regular cleansing and the use of a light moisturiser to keep the skin looking clear and healthy. As you grow older, normal skin can become prone to dryness and therefore requires a richer moisturiser.

Herbal healers Elderflower, marshmallow, marigold, and lavender
Essential oils Geranium, lavender, palmarosa, frankincense, and rose

SKIN CARE: THE BASICS

Whatever skin type you have, it benefits from regular attention, care, and a daily regime. The skin on your face is thin and delicate compared to the rest of your body, so be careful with it. Find products and a regime that suit you, referring to the skin type information in this chapter.

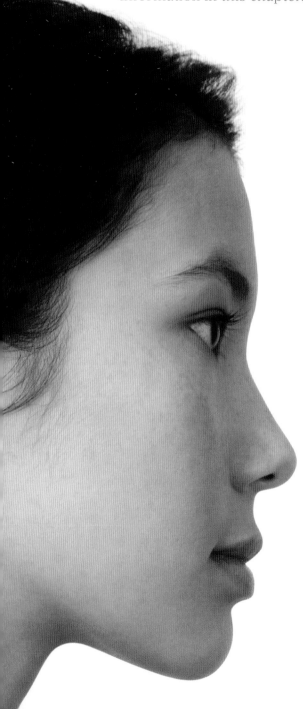

CLEANSE

Cleanse your skin thoroughly, morning and night. Do not use harsh cleansers or scrub vigorously. Use certified organic products to ensure that your cleanser is free from many of the harsh detergents and preservatives that may irritate your skin, and rinse well. If you use an oil-based cleanser, try a muslin or microfibre cloth to remove all traces of make-up and grime, as well as traces of cleanser. Gently pat the skin dry, rather than rubbing it.

TONE

Although many think that applying toner is optional, it is an important step, whether you use a simple herbal water or floral water, or something more complex. A good-quality organic toner – one rich in nourishing herbal extracts and antioxidants, and free from alcohol and harsh preservatives – helps to rebalance the skin after washing and prepares the skin for your moisturiser. If you exercise, refresh your face with toner afterwards. Sweat can clog your pores, making your skin look blotchy and aggravating existing skin conditions, such as acne.

MOISTURISE

All skin types need moisture, even skin prone to oiliness and/or acne. A good moisturiser helps to keep skin healthy, toned, and supple. Choose a moisturiser that suits your skin. Normal or combination skin only needs a light lotion, whereas skin prone to dryness benefits from a rich cream. Oily skin responds best to a gel-based product. Whatever your skin type, at night, you should use a nourishing serum to help restore skin as you sleep. Use certified organic products to ensure your skin gets everything that it needs, and none of the synthetic chemicals that it doesn't.

APPLY A MASK

A good facial mask once or twice a week is more than just a treat. It can deep cleanse, rejuvenate, rebalance, and intensely nourish the skin, leaving it feeling bright and radiant. Avoid harsh or synthetic masks with unnecessary colours and preservatives. Instead, make a simple mask yourself from mineral clays, or choose products made from high-quality herbal extracts with antioxidant properties, as well as skin-loving ingredients like essential fatty acids that can help to reinforce the skin's natural defence and repair mechanisms.

EXFOLIATE

Gently exfoliate once or twice a week to lift dull, old skin cells and stimulate the production of new cells, mimicking the natural cycle of healthy skin (see pp8-9). Exfoliating reveals skin that is softer and more radiant, making your moisturiser and masks more effective. Use a good-quality scrub or polish that does not demand vigorous rubbing – this is counterproductive, especially for delicate facial skin. Avoid harsh chemical peels and opt for products that use natural ingredients, such as oats, crushed seeds, and clays.

Make your own Honey and oat scrub. It will exfoliate your face gently, leaving the skin soft, smooth, and hydrated.

PROTECT FROM THE SUN

Many face moisturisers contain sunscreen. If you spend most of your day indoors, this ingredient is not necessary – it simply adds to the chemicals on your skin. Most women apply their moisturiser only once in the morning. If you are outside all day, this renders the sunscreen useless as you must re-apply it regularly for it to be effective.

   If you spend all day outdoors, a good-quality organic and mineral-based sunscreen is a must. This is the case even if it is cloudy or cold, as the sun's rays can reflect off water, sand, and snow. Far from a healthy glow, a tan is the skin's attempt to prevent sun damage. When a tan turns to a burn, that damage – which raises the risk of developing skin cancer – has been done.

THE TRUTH ABOUT SPF

Most of us are aware of the Sun Protection Factor (SPF), but very few of us understand how it works. You might think that SPF 30 gives you twice the protection of an SPF 15, but this is not the case, because the SPF scale is not linear. No sunscreen can block all the sun's rays, but if you have sensitive skin that is prone to burning, a few extra percentage points (see the scale, right) can make a difference. Never rely on sunscreen as your only method of protection; seek shade during the middle of the day, and wear protective clothing and a hat when you can.

THE SCALE

SPF 15
blocks 93% of UVB rays

SPF 30
blocks 97% of UVB rays

SPF 50
blocks 98% of UVB rays

DRY SKIN

Delicate and susceptible to flaking and fine lines, dry skin simply does not retain moisture well. It can produce uncomfortable symptoms, such as itchiness or tautness after washing. In rare cases, it leads to eczema, psoriasis, cracks, fissures, and infection. Dry skin is often a feature of genetics, but as we age, it is more common, as the skin produces less oil.

TRY...

Enjoy a gentle beauty regime. Use a sensitive cleanser that does not contain alcohol or fragrance, as these may contribute to dryness. When you wash your skin, rinse it with a generous quantity of tepid–warm water. Do not use hot water because it removes natural oils from your face that help to keep it hydrated. Gently exfoliate once a week to remove dead skin cells. Avoid salt and sugar scrubs and instead look for products that give a "soft" scrub, such as oatmeal – ideal as it will not stress the skin. Oatmeal also contains saponins (plant-based cleansers) that gently remove oil, dirt, and dead skin cells.

USE GENTLE and mild soaps or cleansers. Avoid deodorant soaps and products that contain alcohol, fragrance, retinoids, salicylic acid, or alpha-hydroxy acid (AHA).

GENTLY DRY your skin by patting with a towel. Do not scrub skin while bathing, or routinely use loofahs (sea sponges) or any other harsh exfoliating bath items.

MOISTURISE with a rich moisturiser immediately after bathing or washing your hands. Ointments or thick creams may work better than lotions, but they may take longer to soak in.

CHOOSE VEGETABLE OIL-based products instead of those based on mineral oils. Re-apply as needed throughout the day.

TRY A HUMIDIFIER and do not let indoor temperatures get too high.

WEAR GLOVES when you go outside in the cold or when you use household cleaning products.

TRY WEARING NATURAL FIBRES and use hypoallergenic laundry detergents as much as possible. Pay attention to everything that sits next to your skin.

VISIBLE LINES
Areas around the forehead and eyes are susceptible to fine lines and wrinkles.

RED OR DRY PATCHES
The cheeks and hairline are likely to be danger zones for patchy, dry, or inflamed skin.

DRY OR FLAKY SKIN
The nostrils may become particularly dry, especially during periods of cold weather.

QUICK FIX

Use virgin coconut oil to treat all dry skin conditions and improve skin health. Try applying it to the skin twice daily to calm inflammation and reduce water loss. Studies show that this affordable oil can help to treat atopic dermatitis – an allergic reaction that causes dry, inflamed skin.

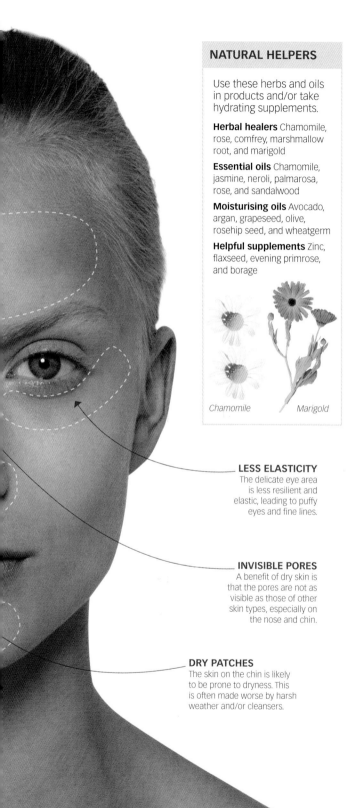

NATURAL HELPERS

Use these herbs and oils in products and/or take hydrating supplements.

Herbal healers Chamomile, rose, comfrey, marshmallow root, and marigold

Essential oils Chamomile, jasmine, neroli, palmarosa, rose, and sandalwood

Moisturising oils Avocado, argan, grapeseed, olive, rosehip seed, and wheatgerm

Helpful supplements Zinc, flaxseed, evening primrose, and borage

Chamomile   *Marigold*

AVOID...

If your skin is very dry, it often does not take much for it to become rough and scaly, especially on the backs of your hands, arms, and legs. However, there are key things to avoid that can help to alleviate the symptoms. When exposed to extreme heat or cold, dry skin can crack, peel, or become itchy, irritated, or inflamed. Although a necessary part of life for many of us, indoor heating and air-conditioning make it worse.

LIMIT BATHS and showers to 5–10 minutes. If your skin is very dry, bathe only once a day. Try to keep the temperature cool.

LIMIT EXPOSURE to extreme weather, such as wind, sun, or cold climates.

NEVER USE SUN BEDS as ultraviolet (UV) radiation from tanning beds and prolonged sun exposure can dry the skin.

LESS ELASTICITY
The delicate eye area is less resilient and elastic, leading to puffy eyes and fine lines.

INVISIBLE PORES
A benefit of dry skin is that the pores are not as visible as those of other skin types, especially on the nose and chin.

DRY PATCHES
The skin on the chin is likely to be prone to dryness. This is often made worse by harsh weather and/or cleansers.

EAT RIGHT FOR MY TYPE

Check any allergies to foods or chemicals. These may produce dry skin, or make it worse – so investigate this by making subtle changes to your diet.

Eat omega-3 fats (found in oily fish, olive oil, nuts, and seeds). These can help to boost skin hydration. There is scientific evidence that taking regular supplements of flaxseed or borage oil can significantly increase skin moisture and reduce rough patches.

Drink water – it is necessary for general skin health. It's not clear from the scientific evidence whether drinking extra water will help your skin retain more moisture, but it certainly helps make it more radiant. Make sure you drink at least 2 litres (3½ pints) of water per day.

Combination Skin

When a complexion is oily in some places and normal–dry in others, it is known as combination skin. Those of us with combination skin may experience blemishes and breakouts at the same time as patches of dry, flaky skin. This skin type benefits from a "combination" approach to skin care, using one type of product and application technique on oily areas of the face, and another on drier areas. You may find that combination skin rebalances itself with simple adjustments to your routine.

TRY...

Many people with combination skin find that they can rebalance it. Are you using something that is too drying or oily, or which contains irritating preservatives, colours, or fragrances? Are you washing or scrubbing too much?

USE MILD CLEANSERS and gentle soaps. Avoid deodorant soaps and products that contain alcohol, fragrance, retinoids, salicylic acid, or alpha-hydroxy acid (AHA).

USE FLORAL WATER, such as rose or orange flower, as a natural toner.

MOISTURISE REGULARLY, but avoid heavy pore-clogging creams and opt instead for lighter lotions.

TRY WATER-BASED COSMETICS instead of oil-based ones. Most organic cosmetics use water in their formulas. Experiment with these to alleviate the oily areas on the face.

AVOID...

Oily or dry skin is sometimes caused by factors that are out of your control, such as your age, genetics, and hormonal changes. However, there are actions you can take to help.

RULE OUT HARSH PRODUCTS, such as non-gentle cleansers and exfoliants – these can make dry areas more dry and encourage oil production in oily areas.

DO NOT WEAR MAKE-UP TO BED – it can encourage spots and breakouts.

LIMIT EXPOSURE to the elements – use a mineral-based sunscreen when it's sunny and wrap up in the cold or wind.

NATURAL HELPERS

Make or buy products that include these herbs and oils. Taking a daily supplement may also help to balance your skin.

Herbal healers Rose, lavender, elderflower, dandelion, burdock, comfrey, yarrow, and calendula

Essential oils Geranium, ylang ylang, bergamot, lavender, palmarosa, frankincense, neroli, rose, and jasmine

Moisturising oils Hazelnut, jojoba, grapeseed, wheatgerm, and avocado

Helpful supplements Vitamin B-complex and zinc

Lavender

SHINY SKIN
Skin is shiny on the forehead, nose, and chin (the T-zone). This may become more pronounced as the day goes on.

VISIBLE PORES
Pores may be overly dilated on areas around the nose and chin.

DRY PATCHES
Red and dry patches are common on the cheeks, hairline, and around the nostrils.

BLACKHEADS
Large pores in the chin and nose areas are prone to clogging, and may be susceptible to blackheads.

SENSITIVE SKIN

Usually dry and prone to flaking, itching, and redness, sensitive skin is also susceptible to allergic reactions and broken capillaries. Anyone of any age or gender is capable of having sensitive skin, but genetics and cultural inheritance play a part. For instance, a number of skin conditions linked to sensitive skin – such as acne, eczema, psoriasis, and rosacea – tend to run in families, and those of Asian descent are especially sensitive to detergents.

TRY...

An allergy test with your doctor helps you to find out what your particular triggers are so you can avoid them. Even if the reasons turn out to be food allergies or intolerances, they can be made much worse by using harsh chemicals on your skin.

PATCH TEST unfamiliar products before you use them.

USE GENTLE natural, organic, and/or hypoallergenic products that are low-foaming and contain very few ingredients. Use them to wash and moisturise twice daily.

APPLY MOISTURISER while your skin is still moist and pat it dry.

AVOID...

The key approach to sensitive skin is "gently does it". Taking care of your skin means learning to avoid the things that can irritate it.

DO NOT TAKE HOT BATHS and showers. Showering or bathing once a day in warm water is frequent enough.

RULE OUT HIGHLY FRAGRANCED soaps, strong detergents, and harsh exfoliants and toners.

DO NOT WEAR MAKE-UP TO BED and if you can, avoid waterproof cosmetics, as these require harsh cleansers to remove.

LIMIT EXPOSURE to extreme temperatures – both indoors and out. Stay out of the sun when you can, and when you can't, use a good-quality mineral-based sunscreen.

NATURAL HELPERS

Make or buy products that include these herbs and oils. You may wish to take a daily supplement to help to calm the skin.

Herbal healers Calendula, oats, green tea, aloe, comfrey, marigold, chickweed, and marshmallow

Essential oils Chamomile, Roman chamomile, lavender, and rose

Moisturising oils Apricot kernel, avocado, almond, jojoba, wheatgerm, rosehip seed, and borage

Helpful supplements Probiotics, omega-3 fats, vitamins B5 and E

Marshmallow

DRYNESS AND SCALING
The hairline and cheeks are prone to dryness and scaling – this problem can be made worse by harsh hair-styling products.

INFLAMED PATCHES
The cheeks and hairline are susceptible to red, bumpy, and inflamed patches. The cheeks may also become itchy, tingly, or feel as if they are burning.

BLUSHING
A tendency towards blushing or large areas of redness is common across the nose and cheeks.

FLUSHING
The skin on the neck may flush as a result of an allergic reaction.

OILY SKIN

Oily skin is often a matter of genetics or hormonal changes. The body produces hormones that lead to oily skin in adolescence, as well as during menstruation, pregnancy, and menopause. These changes trigger the body to produce more oil, which combines with dead skin cells to clog pores, but also moisturises and makes you less prone to wrinkles.

TRY...

Oily skin is likely to be a little lifeless, heavy, and prone to pimples and acne. You cannot do much about the hormonal changes that trigger oiliness, but there are lots of other changes you can make. Use a gently astringent beauty regime that helps to balance the skin and keep the pores clear.

CLEANSE TWICE DAILY, morning and night. Regular cleansing is a must in order to keep the pores clear and reduce a build-up of sebum. Do not scrub hard or make your skin "squeaky clean", and thoroughly rinse the product off the skin.

USE AN ASTRINGENT TONER, which helps to control oil and shine throughout the day. If you have been perspiring heavily, give your face a wipe with toner to ensure pores remain clear.

USE "NONCOMEDOGENIC" PRODUCTS – if they are labelled as such it means they do not contain any pore-clogging ingredients.

KEEP A SPRAY BOTTLE of gently astringent witch hazel herbal water or orange flower water on hand to spritz your face during the day.

TRY WATER-BASED COSMETICS instead of oil-based ones. Most organic cosmetics use water in their formulas. Experiment with these to alleviate the oily areas on the face.

MOISTURISE, as even oily skin needs hydrating. Choose light lotions over heavy creams or look for oil-free moisturisers.

ADJUST TO THE SEASONS as oiliness can change depending on the weather. Use a lighter cleanser in cold weather when skin is a bit dry, and use a deep-cleansing product in the warmer months.

WHAT'S CAUSING MY BREAKOUT?

In adulthood, acne and spots are linked to more than simply oily skin or normal hormonal changes. They can also be linked to poor diet or environmental toxins and may be a side effect of other conditions, such as sluggish liver function or polycystic ovaries. Although it may not seem an obvious trigger, stress could be the cause of your problem skin. Stress – whether physical or emotional – can cause oily skin and breakouts. In addition to your skin-care routine, make sure you find time to relax and de-stress.

BLACKHEADS, PIMPLES, AND OTHER BLEMISHES
The chin, nose, and forehead have large pores that are prone to clogging with dirt and oil. These areas may also be susceptible to blemishes.

NATURAL HELPERS

Use these herbs and oils in products. You can also try skin-balancing supplements.

Herbal healers Elderflower, witch hazel, yarrow, and lemongrass

Essential oils Cedarwood, cypress, vetiver, patchouli, orange, and lemon

Moisturising oils Hazelnut, jojoba, argan, and grapeseed

Helpful supplements Vitamins A, B3, and C, zinc, evening primrose, and probiotics

Elderflower

Yarrow   Witch hazel

SHINY PATCHES

The forehead, nose, and chin are susceptible to shiny patches. This may become more pronounced in the afternoons, if you feel stressed, or if the weather is hot.

ENLARGED PORES

The nose and chin may show enlarged pores. These contribute to excess oil production and hard-to-control areas of shine.

QUICK FIX

Clay masks temporarily draw oil and dirt from the pores, leaving oily skin looking fresher for several hours afterwards. As with any kind of skin treatment, you can overuse masks, so keep their use down to once or twice a month or before special occasions when you need your skin to look especially good.

AVOID...

Many products strip the skin of essential oils and are too harsh for oily skin. Do not be tempted to deep-clean your skin, as it is delicate and requires caring treatments.

AVOID HARSH CLEANSERS or toners. These can irritate the skin and cause breakouts.

LEAVE SPOTS ALONE – do not pick, pop, or squeeze them, as this increases redness and inflammation and extends the healing time.

DUMP THE GADGETS. Harsh electronic brushes or super scrubbers, marketed as quick ways to deep-clean skin, can strip the skin of oils and trigger higher oil production as the skin tries to rebalance itself.

EAT RIGHT FOR MY TYPE

Scientists struggle to determine whether certain foods can be conclusively linked to oily or problem skin. Many foods, such as chocolate, coffee, milk, or high-fat foods like French fries, have been linked to oily skin, but there is no consistent link between any food and problem skin.

Be healthy A diet that is high in fat, processed foods, sugar, salt, and additives may promote the kind of inflammation that leads to breakouts. Make sure you're getting all the nutrition you need to promote healthy skin (see pp30-31).

Consume probiotics Your skin reflects your gut health. Eating foods high in probiotics, such as yogurt, can balance oily skin.

MATURE SKIN

It is easy to fall into the trap of believing that the goal of mature skin care is to make you look younger. Exaggerated promises, such as "look 10 years younger overnight" or "quickly reduce all signs of ageing", sound too good to be true because they are. Looking healthy and the best you can for your age is a much more sensible and achievable goal.

TRY...

Your skin is the first organ in the body to show the signs of ageing. As a general rule, the more sensibly you care for your skin and your overall health throughout your life, the better you can withstand the ageing process. Alter your beauty regime to accommodate the changes in your skin.

MOISTURISE, DAY AND NIGHT. Buy products aimed at your particular skin type and needs.

A GOOD SUNCREAM can help to protect your skin. Opt for organic and mineral-based products without chemical contaminants.

LET YOUR SKIN BREATHE – go without make-up when you can, get plenty of fresh air to help oxygenate the cells of the skin, and exercise to encourage sweat and the release of toxins.

THE SKIN AROUND YOUR EYES is very delicate and becomes more so as you age. Use products specially designed for those areas – and pat them into the skin, without rubbing.

GET ENOUGH SLEEP – it costs nothing and studies show that lack of sleep can age your appearance by as much as 10 years.

FOR AN EXTRA BOOST when you really need to look your best, why not opt for a facial massage. You can book time with a professional therapist or learn how to do it yourself (see pp28–29).

QUICK FIX

To prevent or minimize the appearance of age spots, use a good-quality mineral-based sunscreen and choose organic products. Lemon and benzoin essential oils have skin-lightening properties. Look out for products containing liquorice (capable of lightening spots) and glycolic acid (a gentle exfoliant derived from citrus papaya).

FIGHT FREE RADICALS

Unstable molecules that attach to skin cells, free radicals are the main cause of premature skin ageing. The body produces them but pollution and synthetic chemicals increase exposure. Antioxidants help to neutralize free radicals, so choose products rich in vitamin E and make sure your diet contains plenty of fresh whole foods.

THINNING
The skin around the eyes and cheeks becomes thinner as we age. This is linked to a loss of elasticity and a dryness that leads to lines and bags.

SAGGING, FINE LINES, AND WRINKLES
As collagen production drops, an associated loss of skin elasticity causes fine lines. Puffiness and bags are also common around the jawline, neck, eyes, and forehead.

DRY PATCHES
Ageing skin is prone to dryness around the forehead, eyes, cheeks and neck. Harsh cleansers and peels make this worse.

NATURAL HELPERS

Use these herbs and oils in products or try taking daily supplements.

Herbal healers Rose, comfrey, marshmallow root, marigold, and white or green tea

Essential oils Frankincense, myrrh, rose, palmarosa, lavender, neroli, and patchouli

Moisturising oils Cocoa butter, apricot kernel, avocado, rosehip seed, and almond

Helpful supplements Vitamins A, C, D, and E, CoQ-10, evening primrose, selenium, and zinc

Rose   *Comfrey*

AVOID...

As we age, our skin undergoes changes – the collagen fibres that are the underlying support structure of the skin become twisted and matted, causing wrinkles and lines. There are some measures you can take to help slow down this inevitable process – the earlier you start, the better your skin will appear later in life.

DO NOT SCRUB THE SKIN as your cleanse. Use a gentle cleanser to remove dirt and make-up twice a day, rinse it thoroughly, and pat dry.

DO NOT SMOKE – it increases free-radical damage that causes premature skin ageing.

DO NOT DRINK TOO MUCH ALCOHOL because it can dry the skin and hasten the appearance of spider veins.

LIMIT SUN EXPOSURE, which hastens collagen damage. Use quality, mineral-based sunscreens and sun blocks.

DO NOT TAKE THE LABEL AS GOSPEL and choose products carefully. Some anti-ageing products, such as skin peels, can end up exaggerating the signs of skin ageing over time.

AGE SPOTS
Also known as liver spots, age spots are tan or dark brown patches that are signs of mature skin's greater susceptibility to UV radiation. They are common on the cheeks and forehead because the face is often exposed to the sun.

SPIDER VEINS
Tiny capillaries near to the skin's surface break to form spider veins (also known as thread veins). These occur on the nose, cheeks, and chin. They also appear during times of hormonal upheaval, such as during pregnancy or the menopause.

EAT RIGHT FOR MY TYPE

Drink water to stay hydrated and keep skin glowing.

Consume healthy fats, such as omega-3 fats (oily fish, nuts and nut oils, and egg yolks) and omega-6 fats (seed and seed oils, wholegrains, evening primrose, and borage oils).

Eat a rainbow. Bright-coloured organic fruit and vegetables, green tea, and dark chocolate are rich in antioxidants that help to fight free radicals.

BEAUTY BALM

FOR ALL SKIN TYPES

Use this indulgent facial balm to **revive** and **nourish** dull or tired-looking skin. Rich oils and shea nut butter help to prevent excessive water loss from the skin, keeping it supple and soft. The balm can **cleanse**, **exfoliate**, decongest, and enrich. It contains argan oil, a Moroccan treatment for skin and hair, and vitamin- and antioxidant-rich rosehip oil, which **regenerates** the skin and **improves** its tone.

INGREDIENTS

ROSEHIP SEED OIL
Rich in vitamins and antioxidants, this oil helps to reduce scar tissue.

BEESWAX
This forms a protective layer on the skin.

CYPRESS ESSENTIAL OIL
Distilled from the needles and twigs of the evergreen tree, this oil has a fresh fragrance.

FRANKINCENSE ESSENTIAL OIL
Toning and rejuvenating properties make this one of the best oils for improving skin tone and treating mature skin and wrinkles.

BERGAMOT ESSENTIAL OIL
This is a refreshing and cooling oil with a sweet fruit scent and skin-healing properties.

SHEA NUT BUTTER
This is a moisturising, protective, and skin-softening butter.

ARGAN OIL
This oil is rich in unsaturated fatty acids and vitamin E.

MAKES 100G (3½OZ)

INGREDIENTS
2 tbsp argan oil
2 tbsp rosehip seed oil
2 tbsp shea nut butter
1 tbsp beeswax
5 drops cypress essential oil
5 drops frankincense essential oil
5 drops bergamot essential oil

HOW TO MAKE

1 Heat the oils, butter, and beeswax, together in a bain-marie, until the wax has melted. Remove from the heat.
2 Add the essential oils and pour into a sterilized jar. Allow to cool for 1–2 hours, before using or applying the lid. Store in a cool, dark place. Keeps for up to 3 months.

HOW TO APPLY

Massage into the skin with circular movements. Leave on for an ultra-rich protective moisturiser, or use as a cleanser and remove with a damp muslin cloth or flannel, to polish away dead skin cells.

Palmarosa Facial Oil

FOR OILY OR COMBINATION SKIN

This blend of light grapeseed, **balancing** jojoba, and hemp oils helps to **revive** and restore the balance to oily or combination skin. Palmarosa essential oil has a sweet, rosy–floral odour and **antiseptic** properties. It is **hydrating** and helps to **normalize** sebum production. Zesty lemon essential oil is an **astringent**, tightening the pores and counteracting overproduction of sebum.

MAKES 90ML (3FL OZ)

INGREDIENTS

60ml (2fl oz) grapeseed oil
1 tbsp jojoba oil
1 tbsp hemp seed oil
5 drops palmarosa essential oil
2 drops bergamot essential oil
2 drops lemon essential oil
1 drop lavender essential oil

HOW TO MAKE

1 Pour the oils into a bowl. Add the essential oils and mix well.
2 Pour into a sterilized bottle and place a tight-fitting lid or dropper on. Shake well before use. Store in the fridge. Keeps for up to 3 months.

HOW TO APPLY

Apply a few drops to the fingertips and massage into the face and neck, using upward-sweeping motions, avoiding the delicate eye area. Use at night or under your everyday moisturiser if your skin is in need of additional hydration.

Brightening Facial Oil

FOR ALL SKIN TYPES

Revive dull and tired skin with this **antioxidant-rich** facial oil. Rosehip oil has been found to be beneficial in tissue **regeneration** for conditions such as burns, facial wrinkles, and treatment of scars. Sea buckthorn oil is rich in essential fatty acids and carotenoids, making it a fantastic oil for **brightening** the skin. It may leave a slight yellowish tinge on the face, but it is easily washed off.

MAKES 60ML (2FL OZ)

INGREDIENTS

2 tbsp rosehip oil
1 tbsp wheatgerm oil
1–2 drops sea buckthorn oil
2 drops cypress essential oil
2 drops clary sage essential oil
2 drops rosemary essential oil
2 drops frankincense essential oil

HOW TO MAKE

1 Pour the oils into a bowl. Add the essential oils and mix well.
2 Pour into a sterilized bottle and place a tight-fitting lid or dropper on. Shake well before use. Store in the fridge. Keeps for up to 3 months.

HOW TO APPLY

Apply a few drops to the fingertips and massage into the face and neck, using upward-sweeping motions, avoiding the delicate eye area. Use at night or under your everyday moisturiser if your skin is in need of additional hydration.

NIGHT-TIME FACIAL OIL

QUICK

FOR ALL SKIN TYPES

Soothe your skin as you sleep with this luxurious, fragrant facial oil. Rich in essential fatty acids, this combination of vegetable oils **nourishes** and **smoothes** the skin as you sleep. The blend of essential oils in this recipe has beneficial actions on the skin: **skin-regenerating** patchouli oil, **balancing** ylang ylang oil, and **soothing** orange essential oil.

MAKES 100ML (3½FL OZ)

INGREDIENTS

1 tbsp pomegranate oil
2 tbsp macadamia seed oil
2 tsp castor oil
3 tbsp jojoba oil
2 drops benzoin tincture
1 drop cypress essential oil
1 drop clary sage essential oil
1 drop patchouli essential oil
1 drop ylang ylang essential oil
1 drop orange essential oil

HOW TO MAKE

1 Pour the oils into a bowl. Add the tincture and essential oils, and mix well.
2 Pour into a sterilized bottle and place a tight-fitting lid or dropper on. Store in the fridge. Keeps for up to 3 months.

HOW TO APPLY

Apply a few drops to the fingertips and massage into the face and neck, using upward-sweeping motions, avoiding the delicate eye area. Use at night to help nourish your skin while you sleep, especially if your skin is in need of additional hydration. You could use this oil as part of a 10-minute facial massage, as shown on pp28-29.

Clary sage
An essential oil is distilled from clary sage's leaves. It cools skin inflammation and may help to treat anxiety.

10-Minute Facial Massage

A weekly facial massage can help to increase circulation, create an even skin tone, lift slack skin, and reduce puffiness. Before you begin, wash and dry your hands. Sit down on a chair comfortably and relax with your feet flat on the floor and your back supported. Throughout the process, always massage in an upwards direction.

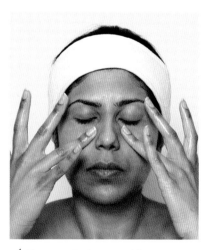

1 Choose a facial oil that is suitable for your skin type. Rub 3 drops of the oil between your fingertips. Hold your hands in front of your nose and inhale into your hands, then exhale deeply. Repeat 3 times.

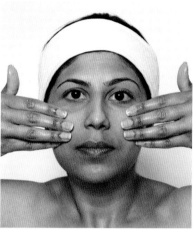

2 Spread the oil over the face, starting under the jaw and moving upwards towards the forehead with gentle but firm sweeping movements, avoiding the delicate eye area. Repeat 3 times.

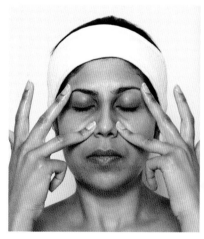

3 Evenly space out the fingertips of the index, middle, and ring fingers along the eyebrows. Gently press and release the fingertips. Move 1cm (1/3in) towards the hairline and repeat.

4 Draw spectacles around the eyes using ring fingers, starting from between the eyes. Repeat 3 times.

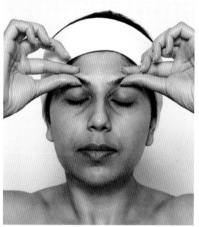

5 Pinch both of the eyebrows. Start from above the nose and move outwards towards the ears. Repeat 3 times.

6 Using the ring fingers, apply small circular movements to the bridge of the nose, moving down towards the nostrils.

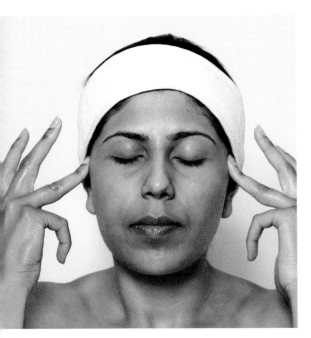

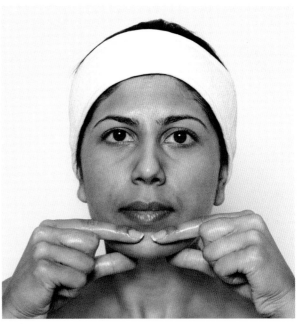

7 Using the ring fingers, apply very gentle pressure underneath the centre of the eyes, moving along the cheekbone towards the ears. Sweep fingers down your neck towards the shoulders.

8 Pinch the chin using the thumb and forefinger of both hands, then sweep along the jaw towards the ears. This helps to invigorate the jaw.

9 Gently tug the ear lobes, then, using both hands, invigorate the face using quick flicking movements with your fingers to get the blood pumping, moving across the jaw and up the cheeks.

10 Finish with deep stroking movements using the full hand and fingers, starting under the jaw and sweeping up the cheeks, around the eyes, and up to the forehead. Repeat 3 times.

EAT WELL FOR... CLEAR SKIN

Our skin is a visible indicator of our health and well-being. A poor diet, lack of nutrients or fluids, stress allergies, or inflammation can show up on the skin as spots, eczema, dullness, or premature ageing. If you want to transform the health of your skin, adapt your diet and you will see the effects in 1–2 weeks. Here are some dietary dos and don'ts and the key superfoods that can contribute to beautiful, healthy skin.

BOOST YOUR BASICS

GET YOUR 7-A-DAY Eat at least 7–10 portions of organic fruit and vegetables a day. This ensures you get enough vitamin C, which has an anti-inflammatory effect and can also boost collagen production. In addition, phytonutrients in fresh fruit and vegetables contain antioxidants that boost skin health and help to prevent skin ageing.

CHOOSE WHOLEGRAIN Whole wheat, oats, and brown rice contain the antioxidant vitamin E, which has a protective effect on skin cells.

DRINK WATER Drinking plenty of water is cleansing for your skin, and helps to rid your body of toxins. It can also help the skin to stay plump and hydrated.

TRY OMEGA-RICH OILS Keep your skin supple and healthy by including "good" oils in your diet, such as those found in fish, nuts, and seeds. Olive, hazelnut, hemp, and flaxseed oils are superb choices. Omega-rich oils also have an anti-inflammatory effect, which is important for clear skin.

EAT ORGANIC Containing fewer toxic pesticide residues, organic food is healthier because it is higher in certain important nutrients, such as zinc – an essential mineral for clear and healthy skin.

SUPERFOODS

Supplement a balanced diet with these superfoods – bursting with the vitamins, minerals, and antioxidants that your skin needs to repair itself, they can dramatically improve your complexion.

CASHEWS
These nuts contain a high level of protein to repair the skin and are a useful source of minerals, such as iron and zinc, that help to heal the skin.

AVOCADOS
This fruit is high in omega-fatty acids, which help to maintain moisture in the epidermal layer of the skin, keeping it soft. They are also a source of oleic acid – involved in regenerating damaged skin cells and reducing inflammation, facial redness, and irritation.

DANDELION LEAVES
Eat fresh greens in a salad or make tea from the dried leaves. Dandelion leaves encourage healthy elimination, thus reducing outbreaks. They are also a source of carotenoids, flavonoids, vitamins A and C, and calcium, iron, and potassium.

GOJI BERRIES
This berry, once known as the "key to eternal youth" due to its regenerative properties, is a powerhouse of antioxidants, and contains vitamins A and E. Eating them can nourish the skin from the inside and help to protect against inflammation.

SAY NO TO...

PROCESSED FOODS These are full of pro-ageing unhealthy fats, salt, and sugars. A diet based on these foods is high in calories but low on the real nutrients your skin needs to stay clear and healthy.

SUGAR AND REFINED CARBOHYDRATES These can quickly make your blood-sugar level soar, triggering your body to produce the hormone insulin to help your cells absorb the sugar. Studies show that insulin plays a role in acne. Embracing a diet with a low-glycemic load can help to clear the skin – to do this, avoid sugar and refined carbohydrates, and completely cut out the worst culprits – fizzy drinks.

TOO MUCH DAIRY There is nothing wrong with a small amount of milk and dairy in a balanced diet, but if you suffer from acne or spots, it can be worth eliminating these from your diet for a while, as some people find that milk is pro-inflammatory. Studies show that going on a dairy-free diet can help eliminate acne.

SMOKING This is not a dietary recommendation but abstaining makes a massive difference to the health of your skin, because smoking wrecks the skin, causing dullness, congestion, and premature ageing.

FLAXSEEDS
These seeds contain the anti-inflammatory fatty acids that are necessary for maintaining healthy, clear skin. Flaxseed oil is particularly good at helping to reduce skin problems involving inflammation, such as eczema or acne. Sprinkle the cracked seeds or drizzle the oil over salads, soups, and stews.

BRAZIL NUTS
Good sources of zinc, brazil nuts also contain selenium, which supports immunity and helps wounds and skin to heal.

ALMONDS
These are high in vitamin E, an antioxidant nutrient that helps to improve the condition and appearance of your skin. Eat a few almonds every day or try almond milk as an alternative to cow's milk.

APPLES
Fresh apples contain vitamins A and C – both helpful for healing the skin and boosting healthy collagen. The compound pectin helps to balance blood sugar and encourage elimination so that skin remains clear.

THE MAGIC OF MAKE-UP

Make-up is the ultimate quick fix and a fantastic way to temporarily transform your look. Many of us feel beautiful and confident when we wear make-up. It is possible to define cheekbones, accentuate or open up the eyes, even out the skin tone, and make lips look full or lashes look long. However, learning to love your face without make-up is the first step towards using make-up positively, as a means to bring out the best in your unique self.

POSITIVE MAKE-UP

Studies show that we still live in a world where most of us perceive women who wear make-up to have qualities that are lacking in those who don't wear it, such as greater competency in the workplace, trustworthiness, and likability. These perceptions can push us into tortuous, high-maintenance fixes – fake tan, false lashes, sculpted brows, and big hair – in order to look good. But there are easy, natural ways to look good and wear make-up that do not require hours of application and regular top-ups.

GO ORGANIC

Conventional make-up products are full of synthetic colours and fragrances, and harsh preservatives that can cause skin problems. It's worth investing in organic and natural cosmetics, which avoid these in favour of mineral colours and natural preservatives, such as vitamin E.

KNOW WHEN YOU DON'T NEED IT

Make-up has become such a part of our lives that many of us do not "choose" to wear it, in any real sense of the word. We wear it because we are expected to, or because we think it makes us look better, or because all the other women we know wear it. Make wearing make-up a positive choice. Ask yourself every once in a while: do I really need to wear make-up today?

KEEP IT CLEAN

Clean your make-up brushes and other tools regularly to keep them free from harmful bacteria. Replace products regularly (even make-up has a sell-by date) and do not share them with others as this can pass viruses and bacteria from one person to another.

REMOVE MAKE-UP AT NIGHT

It may be tedious, especially if you are tired, but removing make-up is the best thing you can do for your skin, since night-time is when the skin repairs and renews itself. Incorporate a little light massage into your facial cleansing routine to help promote good circulation and enhance the tone and texture of your skin.

AVOID TANNING PRODUCTS

Although you might think that a fake tan is a better option than sunbathing, many products contain dihydroxyacetone (DHA), a chemical that, according to research, accelerates skin-cell death and has the potential to cause genetic alterations and DNA damage.

ACCEPT CHANGES

As you age, your skin tone changes and the colours you wore when you were younger don't look the same. Don't be afraid to refresh your look and palette from time to time to suit these changes. Be aware that too much make-up can make you look older – not younger.

USE MAKE-UP SENSITIVELY

If you have skin problems, the ingredients in your make-up could be the cause. If your skin is irritated and red, spending a few days without make-up can help it to recover faster. Re-introduce products one at a time to determine which products you are reacting to. Do not wear eye make-up if you have an eye infection and once this has cleared up buy new make-up to avoid re-infecting the area.

10-MINUTE FLAWLESS FOUNDATION

The key to an even, flawless foundation is good skin. If you don't take care of your skin, make-up is hard to apply and won't last the day. If you follow a cleanse, tone, an moisturise routine, exfoliate twice a week, and use a mask when you can; you won't need to apply too much foundation and your skin will appear luminous and healthy.

LIQUID

Use an organic foundation to limit the toxins that make contact with your skin. Begin with foundation, blending thoroughly, before you apply concealer, powder, contouring powder, and highlights, if desired (see box, opposite).

THE RIGHT SHADE

Liquid foundation Apply a stripe of foundation along the side of your face and jawline. After a few seconds, if the colour is right for you, it will disappear and blend seamlessly into the skin. Don't be tempted to choose a shade darker than your neck. If you feel you are too pale, use bronzer on the neck and face.
Concealer Choose a concealer that has illuminating ingredients to lift any areas of darkness.
Contouring powder Use a matte powder in cool colours – taupe for pale skin tones, grey–brown for medium tones, and cool chocolate-brown for dark tones.

TOOLS

You need just a few tools to achieve a perfect base using liquid or powder products.

Foundation brush

Powder brush

Angled brush

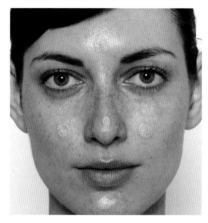
1 Dot a small amount of foundation onto your forehead, nose, chin, and cheeks and begin to blend with a foundation brush. You could also use your fingers or a sponge.

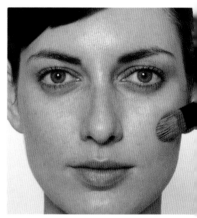
2 Continue to blend. If you find you have applied too much foundation, blot with a clean tissue. By the time you have blended out to the hairline there should be hardly any product left.

4 To conceal blemishes, use another concealer with a slightly thicker consistency. Apply with your finger, a cotton bud, or a small brush. Blend by patting gently with your ring finger.

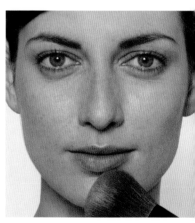
5 Dust lightly with powder where you need it. Most people need it on their T-zone (forehead, nose, and chin). Too much powder shows up fine lines and wrinkles, so use it sparingly.

HIGHLIGHTING

Emphasize the cheekbones, the inner corner of the eyes, the browbone, and the cupid's bow of the lips using a little highlighting powder that has a satin sheen. Beware that highlighting may accentuate fine lines and wrinkles.

MINERAL POWDER

Free from harmful ingredients, mineral powders adhere to the natural oils in the skin, allowing it to breathe. They are perfect for sensitive skin and won't irritate acne-prone skin. Before you apply the powder, moisturise your face, then wait a few minutes for the lotion to sink in. Follow this sequence with contours and highlights, if desired.

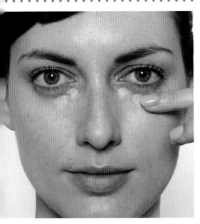

3 Dot a little lightweight concealer under the eye from the inner corner to three-quarters of the way across. Pat with the ring finger until the product blends seamlessly. Apply more if needed, but not too much or eyes can look puffy and dry.

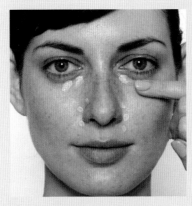

1 Conceal blemishes and circles under the eyes, as shown in steps 3 and 4 opposite. To use mineral powder concealer, tap a little in the lid. Swirl a brush in the product, tap off excess, and gently sweep over the areas.

2 Mineral foundation goes a long way, so start by pouring only a little powder into the product lid. Swirl a large, dense powder brush in the powder. Tap off excess and sweep the brush on the cheekbone.

6 Use an angled brush to sweep contouring powder under the cheekbones. Stop directly below the outer corner of your eyes, otherwise it may look "muddy". Blend well. Finish by brushing on highlights, if desired (see box, above).

3 Using large, round swirling movements, buff the brush over your cheek all the way up to your forehead. Buff the other cheek, then down the nose and chin. The more you buff the greater the coverage.

4 Mineral foundation has a radiant sheen. If you have oily skin or think it looks reflective, use a setting powder for a matte finish. Dip a powder brush into a pressed or loose powder, tap off excess, and apply where necessary.

GET THE LOOK AIR

This fresh look requires light make-up. Air make-up is about suggestion and weightlessness, so use very little product and set aside around 10 minutes for crisp and pure results. The look works best with groomed brows, so brush them through with a clean mascara wand or brow brush. Before you begin, apply a foundation base (see pp34–35).

TOOLS

Medium eyeshadow brush

Small eyeshadow brush

Blusher brush

Lip brush

EYES

BASE Take a medium eyeshadow brush and apply rose mineral blusher over the eyelids. Blend above the eyelid and into the socket line. Using a smaller brush, apply the colour along the lower lash line.

EXPERT TIPS

To get the brow shape right, place a thin pencil or make-up brush along the side of the nostril, facing upwards, towards the brow. Do not bring the brow further in than this line. Then swing the pencil out from the side of the nostril to the outer corner of your eye. Do not bring the brow further out than where this line hits the brow.

Play with your cosmetics. Mineral blusher isn't the only versatile product. You could pat on a little lipstick on your cheeks as blusher, or use eyeshadow instead of brow powder.

ADAPTING FOR YOUR SKIN TONE

Mineral blusher Soft pink and peach colours work on pale skin tones; rose and tawny browns work well on medium skin tones; and russets, burnt sienna shades, and chestnut suit dark skin tones.

Brows
Where there are gaps in your eyebrows, apply a brow pencil or powder in a shade slightly lighter than your hair colour. A brow pencil gives a precise line. A small angled brush dipped in a brow powder gives a softer look.

CHEEKS

BLUSH Lightly swirl a blusher brush in the same mineral blusher used on the eyes. Tap off the excess. Start off light and build up to a lovely fresh glow. Use soft, circular movements starting in the centre of your cheek and blending back. Avoid getting any product in your hairline.

LIPS

ENHANCE Add a touch of lip balm to help your lips look soft and hydrated. Using a lip brush, apply a pale rose–pink shade of gloss to subtly enhance them, making them look full and moisturised.

PEPPERMINT AND SEA SALT INVIGORATING BODY SCRUB

FOR ALL SKIN TYPES

This **invigorating** body scrub gives skin a very firm scrub that can remove dead skin cells, **revive** the circulation, and leave skin silky smooth. Grapefruit essential oil is a lymphatic stimulant with diuretic and **detoxifying** properties that may help with water retention and cellulite. If you want a less abrasive scrub, use table salt instead of sea salt. You could also replace the fresh mint with dried.

INGREDIENTS

ALMOND OIL
This oil adds nourishment to the scrub.

PEPPERMINT ESSENTIAL OIL
This can stimulate the circulation.

FRESH MINT
Gently exfoliating, fresh mint has a crisp scent.

GRAPEFRUIT ESSENTIAL OIL
This oil contains detoxifying properties.

SEA SALT
This is a cleansing, invigorating exfoliant.

MAKES 100ML (3½FL OZ)

INGREDIENTS

4 tbsp sea salt
1 tsp fresh mint
4 tbsp almond oil
5 drops peppermint essential oil
2 drops grapefruit essential oil

HOW TO MAKE

1 Place the sea salt, mint, and almond oil in a bowl.
2 Add the essential oils and mix together to make the scrub. Transfer to an airtight container and store in a cool, dry place. Keeps for up to 6 months.

HOW TO APPLY

Rub into the skin, massaging into any areas of sluggish circulation. Rinse off in the shower or in the bath – as the sea salt dissolves in water, you can enjoy a relaxing mineral bath. Do not use on freshly shaved skin.

10-MINUTE DRY BODY BRUSHING

Slough off dead skin cells and boost your skin with a weekly brush. The pressure on the skin and the direction you brush in help to move lymph fluid around the body, boosting your natural elimination process and circulation at the same time. Always brush in an upwards direction, and follow each stroke with a sweep of your hand.

TOOLS

Use a firm-bristled brush. A long handle helps you to reach the whole body. If you prefer, choose one with a strap handle that helps you to control pressure.

WHY BODY BRUSH?

Dry brushing stimulates and energizes the body, so it is best to do it in the morning before you shower. Regular brushing helps to deliver oxygenated blood to the skin and helps it to hydrate efficiently, contributing to a healthy skin tone. Dry brushing also helps to eliminate toxins, so can smooth unsightly lumps and bumps.

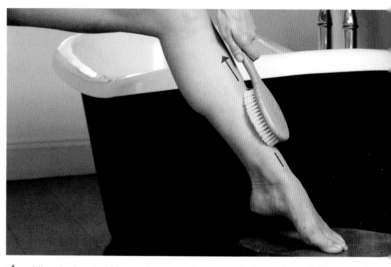

1 Holding the brush with your left hand, brush up the front of your left leg. Use long, sweeping strokes in an upward direction. Brush firmly, but not hard enough to damage the skin. Follow each stroke with a sweep of your right hand. Repeat 3 times.

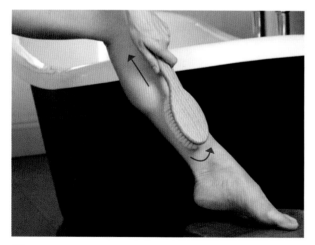

2 Using small, circular movements with your brush, travel up the inside of the same leg, starting at the ankle and moving up to the groin. Follow each stroke with a sweep of your right hand. Repeat 3 times, then switch to the outside of the leg, moving up the leg with the same small, circular movements.

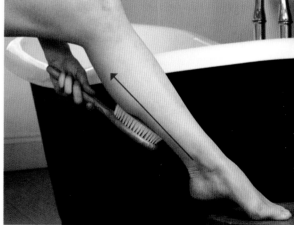

3 Move to the back of the leg, and use long sweeping strokes from the heel to the top of the thigh. Repeat twice, and on the third stroke, continue around the buttock and up towards the back. These movements accelerate the flow of lymph towards the glands where it is eliminated, stimulating your circulation.

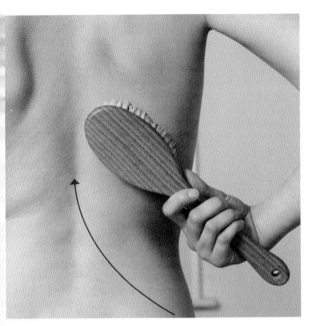

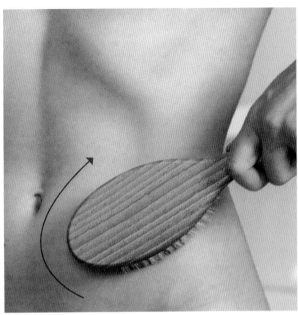

4 Move the brush across the buttocks and up onto the centre of the back, using large, sweeping, circular strokes into the centre of the body. After every stroke, put down the brush and follow the same route with your hand. Repeat 3 times.

5 Move the brush around the side of your body to your front torso, using long, circular strokes across the abdomen. After every stroke, put down the brush and follow the same route with your hand. Repeat 3 times.

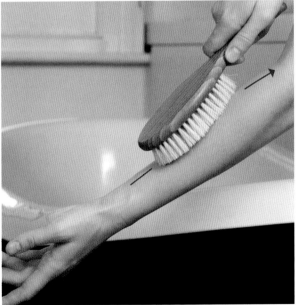

6 Passing the brush to your right hand, use long, sweeping movements to brush the outside of the left arm upwards towards the shoulder, and sweep around the outside of your left breast. After every stroke, put down the brush and sweep along the same route with your hand. Repeat 3 times.

7 To finish, brush the inside of the left arm up towards the armpit, using long, sweeping movements. After every stroke, put down the brush and sweep along the arm with your hand. Repeat 3 times. Repeat the whole sequence on the right-hand side of the body. Afterwards, your skin will feel soft and smooth.

NEROLI SOLID PERFUME

FOR ALL SKIN TYPES

This blend of citrus and spice works as a lovely day-to-night **fragrance**. The freshly fragrant top notes of neroli and bergamot work with a **sweet–citrus** middle note of orange and the **spicy** base notes of frankincense. Two **sweet-smelling** tinctures work as fixatives in the perfume – helping to keep the scent on your skin for as long as possible.

INGREDIENTS

BEESWAX
This creates a waxy base consistency.

PROPOLIS TINCTURE
This rich tincture helps to fix the fragrance.

NEROLI ESSENTIAL OIL
This is a light and refreshing oil with a floral top note.

BENZOIN TINCTURE
This tincture works as a fragrance fixative.

ORANGE ESSENTIAL OIL
This sweet, fresh oil has a citrussy middle note.

SUNFLOWER OIL
Non-fragrant, this works as a consistency agent.

BERGAMOT ESSENTIAL OIL
This is a sweet, citrussy oil with a fruity top note.

FRANKINCENSE ESSENTIAL OIL
This oil supplies a fresh, spicy, citrussy base note.

MAKES 30G (1OZ)

INGREDIENTS

10g (¼oz) beeswax
2 tsp sunflower oil
1 tsp propolis tincture
1 tsp benzoin tincture
8 drops neroli essential oil
4 drops bergamot essential oil
4 drops orange essential oil
2 drops frankincense essential oil

HOW TO MAKE

1 Heat the beeswax and oil together in a bain-marie, until the wax has melted. Remove from the heat.
2 Add the tinctures and essential oils, and mix thoroughly.
3 Pour into a sterilized jar or tin. Once cool, apply to the skin and place the lid on. Store in a cool, dry place. Keeps for up to 6 months.

HOW TO APPLY

Rub onto your pulse points when you need a fragrance boost.

COCONUT CONDITIONER

FOR OILY HAIR

This coconut conditioner leaves the hair feeling soft and light. Coconut is often used in hair care – the oil **softens** the hair and **soothes** the scalp, and its milk has similar **conditioning** and **nourishing** effects on the hair. Egg yolk has long been used to improve the condition of hair. It can **strengthen** hair as well as **moisturise** and condition it.

MAKES ENOUGH FOR ONE APPLICATION

INGREDIENTS

1 egg yolk
1 tsp solid coconut oil
3 tbsp coconut milk

HOW TO MAKE

1 Using a hand-held whisk or stick blender, whisk the egg yolk and coconut oil together in a bowl until frothy.

2 Add the coconut milk and mix until smooth.

3 Pour into a squeezy bottle for easy application. Store in a cool, dry place. Keeps for up to 6 weeks.

HOW TO APPLY

Apply to hair and massage into the scalp. Leave for 2–5 minutes. Rinse with cool water. Dry and style hair as normal.

Massage Your Scalp

Use this simple sequence to massage the conditioner into your hair and invigorate your scalp, promoting healthy, strong hair.

- Gently massage the whole of the head with thumbs and fingers in a "shampooing motion".
- Grasp fistfuls of hair at the roots and tug from side to side, keeping the knuckles close to the scalp.
- Squeeze the temples with the heel of the hands and make slow circular movements.
- Find the occipital bone – the bone you can feel at the back of your head towards the top of your neck. Place the left thumb under the left occipital area and the right thumb on the right occipital area. Use a rubbing movement to release the muscles.

Egg yolk
Nutritionally rich, egg yolk contains protein, vitamins, and minerals. It is also perfect for treating acne and dry, flaky skin.

CHAMOMILE DETANGLER

FOR ALL HAIR TYPES

This combination of chamomile and coconut milk helps to **condition** and **smooth** the hair. Chamomile infusions have been used for years for their medicinal benefits. They can **brighten** up blonde hair and lighten darker shades, and are also very good at **soothing** irritated scalp. Coconut milk is **conditioning** and **nourishing** and acts as a natural detangler for the hair.

INGREDIENTS

CHAMOMILE FLOWERS
These can calm and soothe an irritated scalp.

COCONUT MILK
This nourishing milk contains conditioning properties.

ROMAN CHAMOMILE ESSENTIAL OIL
Beautifully fragrant, chamomile oil is calming to the scalp.

MAKES 200ML (7FL OZ)

INGREDIENTS
200ml (7fl oz) mineral water
1 tbsp chamomile flowers
2 drops Roman chamomile essential oil
2 tbsp coconut milk

HOW TO MAKE

1 To make the chamomile flower infusion, boil the mineral water. Place the flowers in a teapot or glass bowl and pour the boiling water over. Leave to steep for 10 minutes, then strain.

2 Add the essential oil to the coconut milk and mix well.

3 Add the coconut milk mixture to the cooled infusion and mix.

4 Pour into a sterilized bottle and place an atomizer on. Store in a cool, dry place. Keeps for up to 6 weeks.

HOW TO APPLY

Shake well before use. Spray on clean wet hair, comb through, and rinse off with warm water or use as a leave-in product.

VITAMINS, MINERALS, AND NUTRIENTS

Essential to the healthy functioning of our body systems, vitamins, minerals, and nutrients help to strengthen hair and nails, build collagen, and keep skin healthy. We should get all the nutrients we need from a good diet, but modern farming and food-processing methods have had a negative impact on nutritional levels in our food. Boost these levels with particular foods or regular supplements.

Vitamin or Nutrient	Functions for Skin, Hair, and Nails	Rich Food Sources	Notes	Average Daily Intake/ Supplemental Range
Vitamin A (Retinol) and Carotenoids	**Vitamin A:** This is a rich antioxidant and is anti-ageing. It helps to produce collagen. **Carotenoids:** Precursors to vitamin A, carotenoids have antioxidant properties and help to protect skin from sun damage.	**Vitamin A:** Fish-liver oils, animal liver, oily fish, egg yolks, whole milk, and butter. **Carotenoids:** Green and yellow fruits and vegetables, green leafy vegetables, peppers, sweet potato, and broccoli.	Animal sources of vitamin A may be much better absorbed than vegetable sources.	**Vitamin A:** ADI: 5,000–9,000IU SR: 10,000+ **Beta-carotene:** ADI: 5–8mg SR: 10–40mg
B-complex Vitamins	These are required for healthy skin, hair, and eyes, as well as a healthy liver and nervous system.	Yeast, animal liver, kidneys, almonds, wheatgerm, brown rice, mushrooms, egg yolk, red meat, and mackerel.	These may be destroyed by refining and processing.	Variable, check individual vitamin B.
Vitamin C (Ascorbic Acid)	This is necessary for antioxidant function. Vitamin C encourages healthier bones, teeth, gums, cartilage, capillaries, immune system, and connective tissue. Important for healing and anti-ageing. Anti-inflammatory.	Acerola cherry, sweet peppers, kale, parsley, green leafy vegetables, broccoli, watercress, strawberries, papaya, oranges, grapefruit, cabbage, lemon juice, elderberries, liver, and mangoes.	This vitamin is unstable to heat and light. Cooking may lead to a 10–90 per cent loss of vitamin C content.	ADI: 75–125mg SR: 250–2,000mg
Vitamin D (Calciferol)	Cancer-protective vitamin D regulates calcium absorption for healthy bones, teeth, hair, and nail growth. It balances hormones and boosts a healthy immune system.	**Vitamin D3:** Fish-liver oils, sardines (tinned and fresh), salmon, tuna, shrimps, butter, liver, egg yolk, milk, and cheese. **Vitamin D2:** Sunflower seeds, spirulina, mushroom, flaxseed, and sprouted seeds.	Vitamin D is synthesized by sunlight on the skin. Vitamin D3 is easier to absorb than vitamin D2.	ADI: 200–400IU SR: 400–3,000IU
Vitamin E (Tocopherol)	This is necessary for antioxidant function, healthy immune system, heart, circulation, and lipid balance. A sex hormone regulator, it has an anti-ageing effect on the skin.	Sunflower seeds, sunflower oil, safflower oil, almonds, sesame oil, peanut oil, corn oil, wheatgerm, peanuts, olive oil, butter, spinach, oatmeal, salmon, and brown rice.	Losses caused by heat and light. Milling/refining flour causes up to 80 per cent loss of vitamin E content.	ADI: 30mg SR: 100–800mg
Bioflavonoids, such as Citrin, Hesperidin, Rutin, and Quercetin	Anti-inflammatory bioflavonoids are necessary for antioxidant function and a healthy immune system. They are good for healthy blood vessels and may help to prevent broken capillaries. Rutin can combat skin redness.	Apples, black and red berries, blackcurrants, buckwheat, citrus fruit, apricots, garlic, green-growing shoots of plants, onions, rosehips, and cherries.	Cooking and processing foods causes a loss in levels of bioflavoid.	ADI: N/A SR: 500–3,000mg
Essential Fatty Acids (Omega Oils)	These acids help to regulate inflammation and hormones. Good for lipid balance, growth, the nervous system, eyes, skin, joints, and metabolism.	Fish-liver oils, oily fish, milk, cheese, flaxseed (linseed) oil, hempseed oil, canola, and walnut oil.	Loss of content is caused by hydrogenation, light, and heat.	3–8 per cent of calories.